First Words STICKER
Activity Book

Have fun learning new words as you
complete the sticker activities in this book.

Pull out the sticker sheets and keep
them by you as you complete each page.
There are also extra stickers to use
throughout the book or anywhere you want!

make
believe
ideas

Make a pizza
Sticker more toppings on the pizza.

Find the missing stickers.

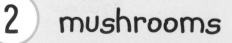 mushrooms

tomato

pepper

Fruity fun

Circle the fruit that is different in each row.

pineapples

pears

oranges

strawberries

3

Stick and match

Use stickers to deliver each flower
to the matching coloured house.

blue

yellow

red

green

Sort the shapes

Draw lines to match the words and shapes.

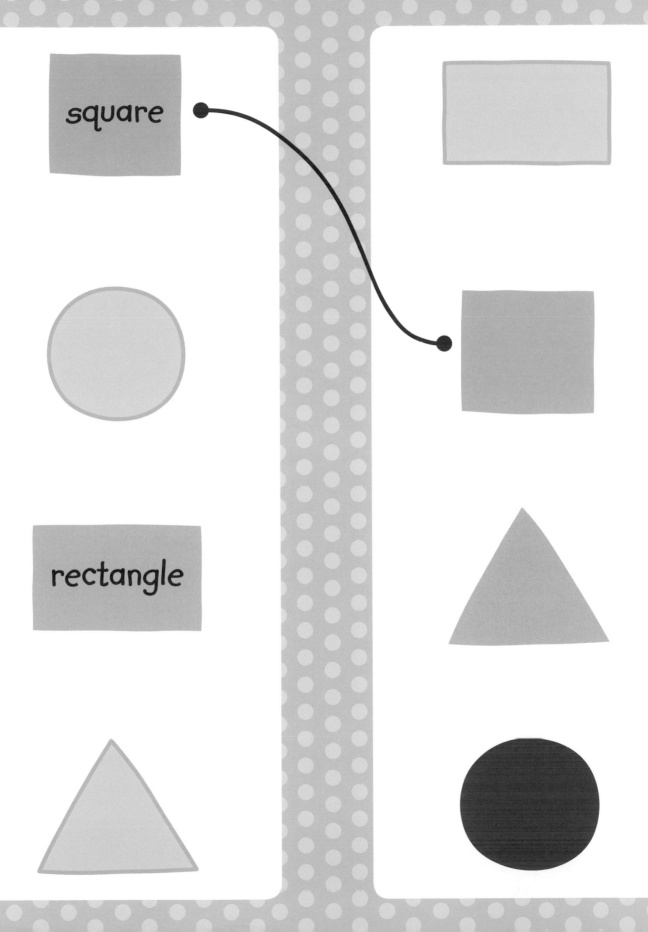

square

rectangle

Forest friends

Sticker an acorn path
for the squirrels.

squirrel   acorn

Colour the flowers.

flowers

bee   worm   bird

ladybird   frog   butterfly

Find the missing stickers to finish each pattern.

How many?

Count the items, then find
the missing stickers and add colour.

1
one

car

2
two

monkeys

3
three

pineapples

8

4
four

kittens

5
five

cupcakes

Home, sweet home

Add stickers to fill the scene.

Look at the scene and
point to the pictures.

car

tree

hot-air balloon

Circle the door.

bird

dog

butterfly

High in the sky
Decorate the hot-air balloon with bright colours.

hot-air balloon

cloud

Flying race

Find the missing stickers and trace the trails.
Who wins the race?

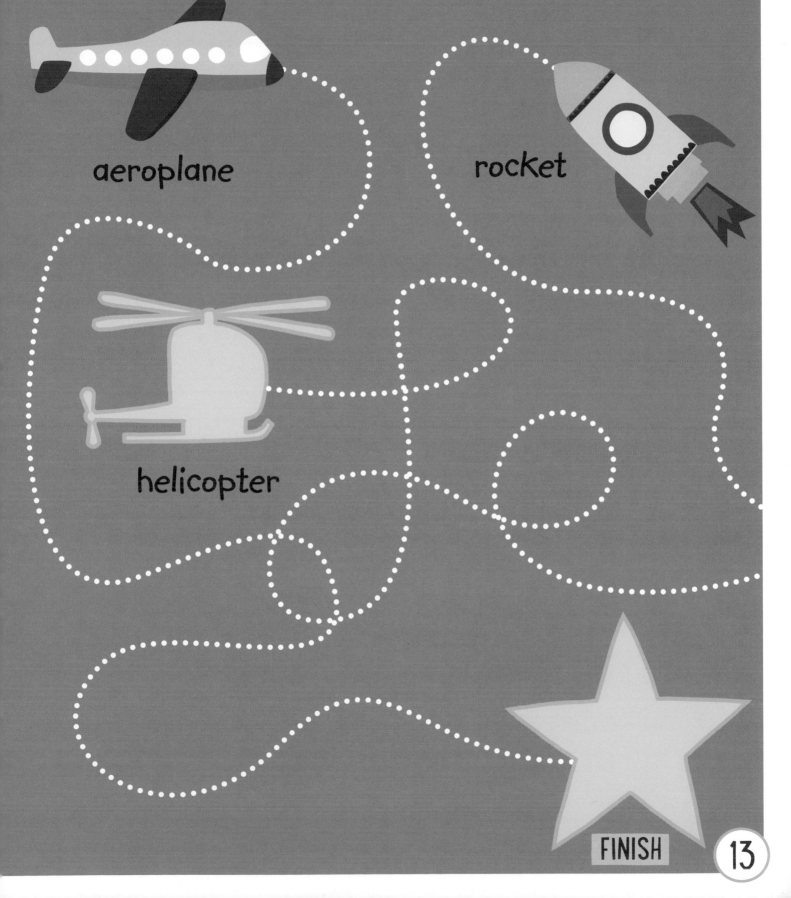

aeroplane

rocket

helicopter

FINISH

Family album

Sticker the missing pictures.

dad

mum

sister

Draw a cute pet here!

brother

Find the difference

Circle five differences between the pictures.

At the zoo

Add stickers to fill the scene.

Look at the scene and point to the pictures.

lion

parrot

zebra

Circle two butterflies.

tiger   monkey   giraffe

Toybox tidy

Sticker the missing toys.

tricycle

paints

castle

crayons

doll

roller skates

robot

18 drum

pirate ship

tea set

Mix and match

Draw lines to match each
word with its opposite.

front

thin

awake

inside

fat

back

outside

asleep

Tall and short

Colour and sticker the animals.

tall

short

On the road

Sticker more vehicles on the busy road.

car

truck

school bus

dustbin lorry

POLICE

Sticker the missing vehicles.

taxi

bicycle

van

motorbike

tanker

police car

Colour the dump truck.

dump truck

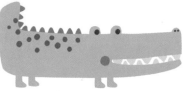

How many?

Count the items, then find
the missing stickers and add colour.

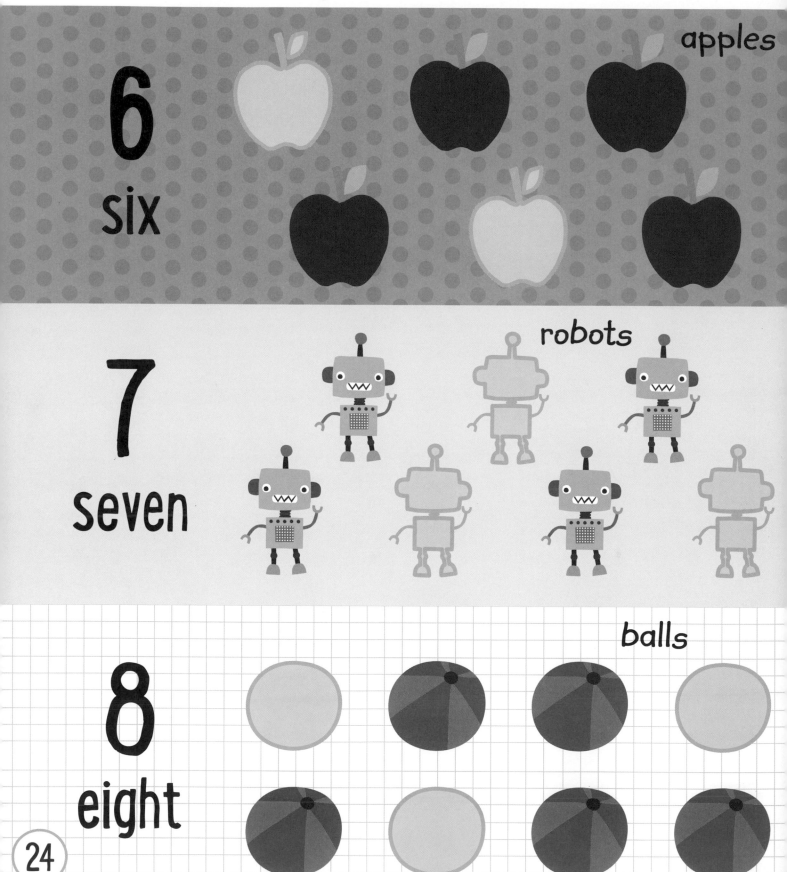

apples

6
six

robots

7
seven

balls

8
eight

24

9 nine rabbits

10 ten chicks

25

Laundry day

Colour and sticker the clothes.

underpants

skirt

shorts

dress

jumper

tights

shirt

Out to dry

Sticker the missing clothes
on the washing line.

Count the items
of clothing, then
sticker the answers.

T-shirts   socks   gloves

Colourful creatures

Colour and sticker the animals.

parrot

rhinoceros

tortoise

peacock

snail

penguin

deer

elephant

28

Mix and match

Draw lines to match each baby to their parent.

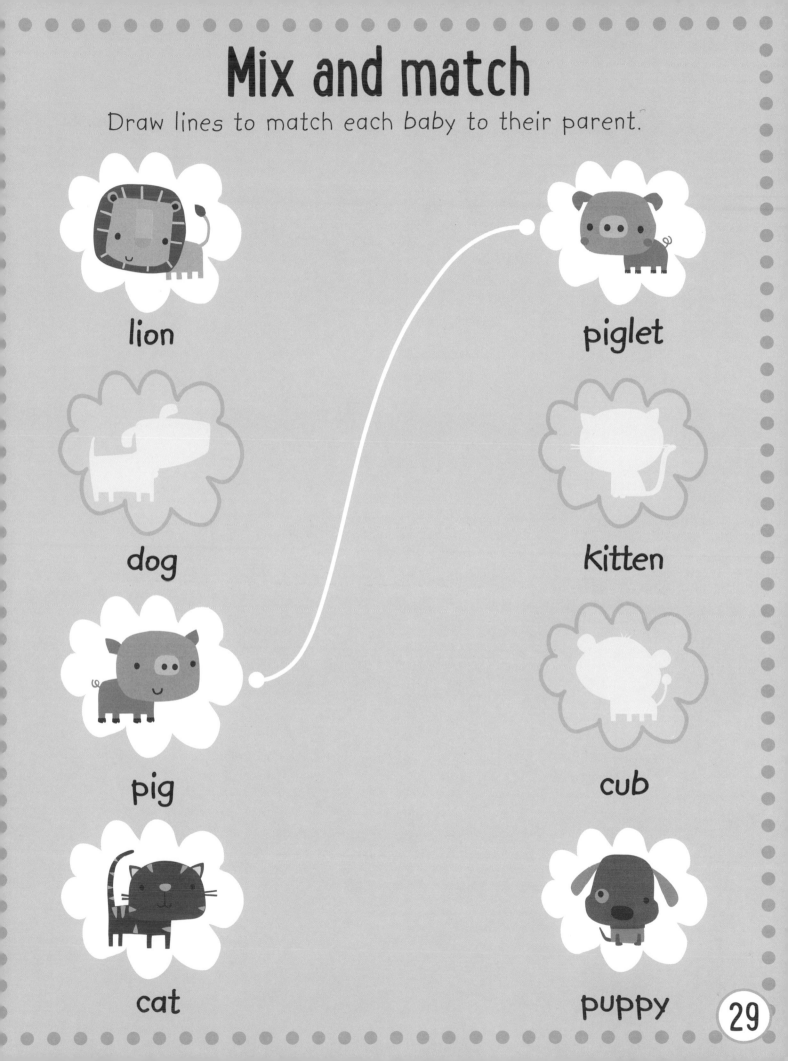

lion

piglet

dog

kitten

pig

cub

cat

puppy

Pretty platefuls

Sticker the food on the matching coloured plates.

red

green

Colour the
fork and knife.

fork   knife

yellow

orange

In the wild

Colour and sticker to finish the scene.

Circle three jellyfish.

shark

jellyfish

penguins

fish

octopus

33

Nee-nah!

Sticker more water over the flames and colour the fire engine.

house

fire engine

Which way?

Guide the ambulance through the maze to reach the family.

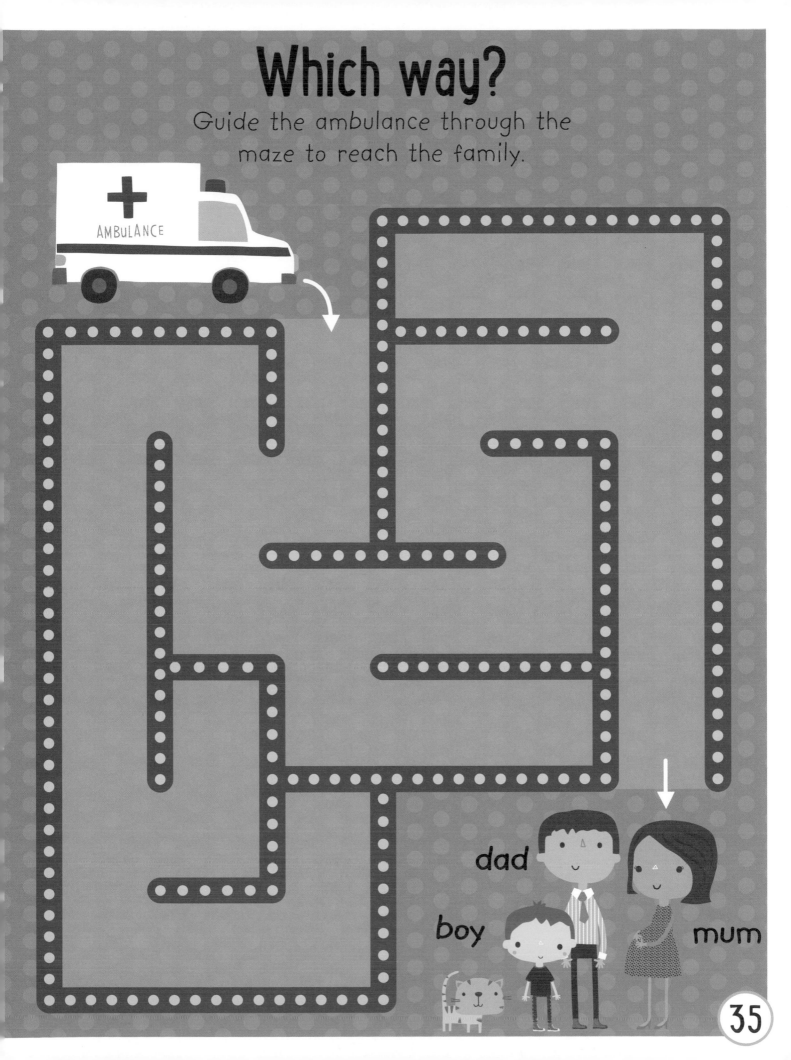

dad

boy

mum

On the farm

Add stickers to fill the scene.

Look at the scene and point to the pictures.

cow

pig

sheep

Circle two cockerels.

tractor

barn

sheepdog

Squeaky clean!

Find the missing stickers.

How many ducks can you spot? Sticker the answer.

bubbles

bath

soap

sponge

hairbrush

Time for bed

Find the missing stickers.

lamp

bed

toys

Can you find these toys in the bedroom?

I dinosaur

I teddy bear

2 pirates

Blast-off!

Sticker the countdown and colour the rocket.

Pages 2-3

Pages 4-5

circle

Pages 6-7

triangle

Pages 8-9

Pages 8-9 continued

Pages 10-11

Pages 13-14

Pages 16-17

Pages 16-17 continued

Pages 18-21

Pages 22-23

Extra Stickers

Pages 22-23
continued

BIG
TRUCK CO.

STOP

Pages 24-25

Pages
26-27

2

4

3

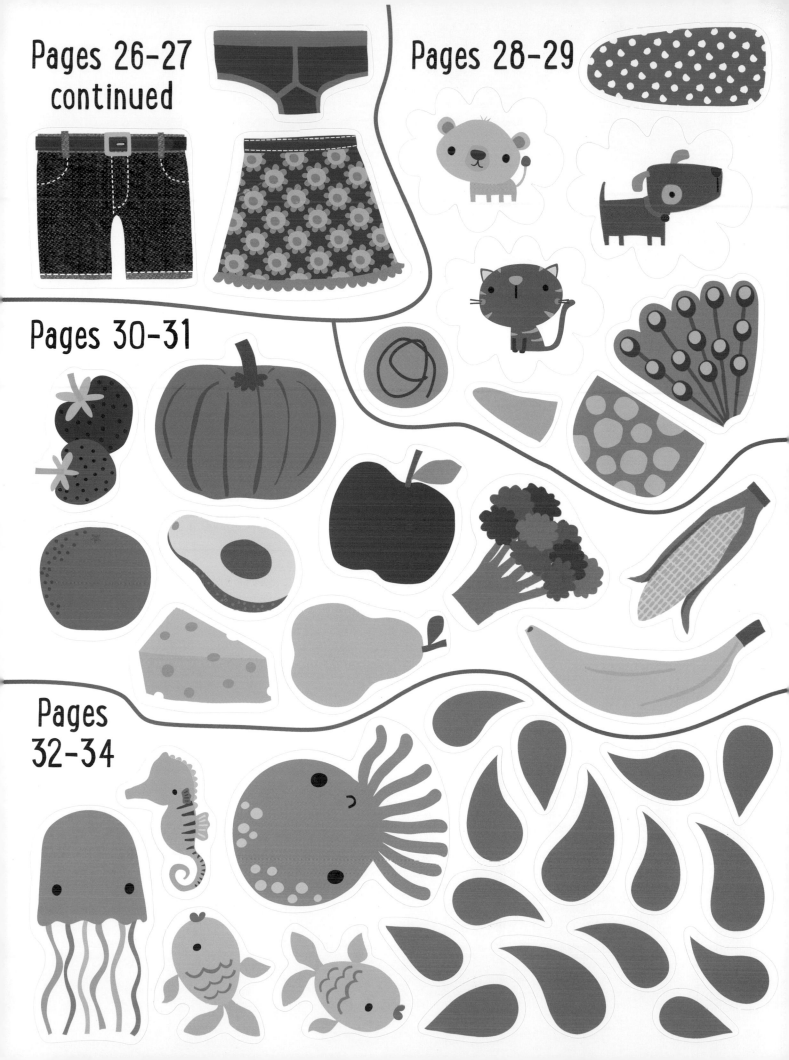

**Pages 26-27
continued**

Pages 28-29

Pages 30-31

**Pages
32-34**

Pages 36-37

Pages 38-40

SOAP

towel

1

2

4

5

Extra stickers